THROUGH
THEIR EYES

INNER VOICES

Edited By Kat Cockrill

First published in Great Britain in 2020 by:

Young Writers
Remus House
Coltsfoot Drive
Peterborough
PE2 9BF
Telephone: 01733 890066
Website: www.youngwriters.co.uk

Printed and bound in the UK by BookPrintingUK
Website: www.bookprintinguk.com
YB0428L

CONTENTS

Tom Walker (15)	66
Lexi Glover (11)	67
Faith Stubbs (13)	68
Owen Shuter (12)	69
Cameron Dawson (13)	70
Tayla-Louise Kinsey (11)	71
Keira Colclough (13)	72
Grace Ainsworth (13)	73
Rehan Abbas Malik (12)	74
Demi-Leigh Davis (13)	75
Megan Lowndes (15)	76
Lily-Rose Moreton	77
Ella Amelia Hughes (13)	78
Olivia Rose Russell (13)	79
Laura Edwards (11)	80
Jemma Gaitley (13)	81
Summer Burton (11)	82
Emily Landers (14)	84
Max Waltho (14)	85
Anya Shelley	86
Lewis Willatt (12)	87
Elliot Sharman	88
Chloe Suzanne Smith (14)	89
Rhuben Robert Johnson (11)	90
Kirsty Jones (15)	91
Bryannah Barnett-Gibson (13)	92
Lexi Ashmall (12)	93
Jamal Winkle (11)	94
Amy Hansbury (14)	95
Shanice Mudzudza (12)	96
Tyler Jones (13)	97
Amelie Barlow (12)	98
Millie Williams	99
Leighton Nixon (12)	100
Grace Leigh (11)	101
Mima Liv Parfitt (12)	102
Lily Pomelli (14)	103
Chloe Challinor (11)	104
Harry Ashton (14)	105
Alecia Ibinson (13)	106
Caitlyn Milward (12)	107
Kimberley Jane Meir (12)	108
Dylan Evans	109

Inaya Jade Bromley (11)	110
Evan Cameron Shallcross (12)	111
Hannah Shingler (13)	112
Frank Turner (14)	113
Tegan Cawley (14)	114
Eleanor Green (12)	115
Miah Brooks (14)	116
Natasha Smith	117
Sophie Poyser (11)	118
Precious Butler (14)	119

Pakefield High School, Pakefield

Ewan Harbord	120
Owen Carson (14)	122
Ayva-Mai Claxton (11)	123
Ryan Griffiths (14)	124
Tori Bellis (12)	125
Darcey Crowe (11)	126
Finley Oliver Gary Chase (12)	127

Rishworth School, Rishworth

Hero Silverwood (11)	128
William Whiteley	129
Ruby Jones (12)	130
Rhianna Lancaster (11)	131
Dorothy Davies (11)	132
Olivia Hambling (11)	133
Lily Elizabeth Edmunds (12)	134
Harry Ashford (11)	135

Sheldon School, Chippenham

Keirabelle St Pierre	136
Milla Smith	137

The Sandon School, Sandon

Harley Donovan (15)	138
Luca Evangelista (14)	140
Georgina Sewell (14)	141
Amy Stone (15)	142
Liam Hodgson (14)	143

Faye Bentley (14)   144
Oliver Guy Newton Agar (14)   145
Samuel Panks (14)   146
Mollie Prior (14)   147
Rachel Ghachaniu (15)   148
Sophia Pilgrim (14)   149
Kade Silverman (14)   150
Owen Griffin (14)   151
Henry Walker (14)   152
Joshua Jones (14)   153

Torquay Boys' Grammar School, Torquay

Ollie Clatworthy (17)   154

THE
POEMS

The Ash Tree

Our love was once like a blooming ash tree,
The golden sun shone brightly above it,
Its lush green leaves were the purest things,
Its authentic beauty could draw tears from thee.

Then, one day, the sun diminished,
Your mocking lies had beat its flames,
These deceitful fables you fooled me with
Had broken every vow you made.

You gambled our love with this cheating game,
But, who can I blame for honesty?
I held you so dear, tied to my soul,
How could you play me so heartlessly?

Now, what can existence mean
When our hearts are ripped through brutally
By those we are most keen upon,
Like the cracked winter leaves
Of a dead ash tree.

Your painted smiles were the fallen things
Coloured in the cold shades of grey and black,
These colours are now all I see,
Like the cracked winter leaves
Of a dead ash tree.

Mahisa Abdul Begum (12)
Bordesley Green Girls' School, Birmingham

An Untold Story

The elephant, a fifty-five million-year-old friend;
Yet, man's evil ways will drive them to their end,
Poaching, trapping, killing, catching
For ivory tusks and pachyderm scratchings.

These priceless artefacts, more than gold,
In the blink of an eye, their body parts sold,
A global crisis with little attention,
Causing many great stress and tension.

For the very few who truly care,
Protestors struggle to be heard,
A genocide of mass proportion,
Will we learn to take heed and caution?

An unstable future,
A fragmented world,
For the many elephants
In their numbers and herds.

Surayyah Amatul Aziz (17)
Bordesley Green Girls' School, Birmingham

Paper-Thin Lies

My truth is clouded in thick white wool,
Pulled over the blinded eyes of the naive,
Where I am The Sun, sanguine, eager and bright,
Muffled by the choking clouds of lies.

When flicking papers are drowned in mutters,
My light flickers yearning to burn their fiction,
In a place where my identity is a 'letterbox' disguise,
And my Daily Mail is the countless judging eyes.

Unlearning self-hate is difficult labour,
When my Guardian angel is still lost at sea -
Navigating between those subdued by fear of the unknown,
Who direct their despair and hatred at me.

When I look in The Mirror, I do not see their villain,
I see a woman. Whose light beams off the shattered glass,
A woman who can outshine and strike down lightning,
No longer afraid to thunder my verity.

Olivia McAnaney (17)
Cronton Sixth Form College, Widnes

A Wide Eye To Fly

Ever since I witnessed one soar,
I was a grey squirrel that had longed for nothing more
Than to spread my wings and take to the sky,
To dazzle and glisten, to be a butterfly,
Instead, I was stuck to my bushy tail and clumsy claws,
Constantly fighting with my bird neighbour in the Great Tree
Wars,
You may think it's a strange ambition,
But, as long as I can remember, it has been my mission
To soar, to be rid of the floor my paws glued me upon,
Or to be a moth, bat or swan.

What I had done in my past lives, I can clearly remember,
My goal from the start to be as light as a feather,
What's the point of memory, you say?
Never wished to be free of the day?
Looking through the eyes of another, simply a new
perspective,
On a quest where my dream is affected,
That time finally came when that previous life came to an
end,
I had finally become what I used to pretend,
Or, so I thought.

Sitting peacefully on my giant branch,
Ready to call the world my ranch,

Cautiously leaning over the edge of the final twig,
I was so small, the sky so big,
Glancing below at my friends, taking off and their graceful descent,
We could fly together until the very end,
The moment I had dreamed of for many past lives,
Finally, my time has arrived,
Learn to never jump ahead of time,
Eyes wide open, look for a sign,
To fulfil our purpose at every moment,
I took a leap of faith and met my opponent,
There was a log plunge, I remember nothing more,
Than being an innocent little caterpillar, broken to the core,
As a pigeon flew towards me before I had a say,
Would've met the sky this time, but I was whisked away.

That's how I learnt to never dwell on the past,
Treasure every second and let my life last,
Live each and every one of those lives to the full,
I had become a worm, kangaroo and bull,
But now I'd finally found my dream in the end.
To live every second until I earned my great ascend,
I never thought I could become my dreaded neighbour,
To heave feathered wings, I could soar, every moment I savour,
A bird I had now learned to be,
Now my eyes are open and I finally can see,
I can never be a butterfly, before being a caterpillar.

Jessica Osborne (13)
Great Sankey High School, Great Sankey

Shadows Of The War

The guns are loading up around me,
I'm trying to escape,
But I just can't be free!

People screaming, struggling, staggering,
I wish that I could help,
But I just can't stop our suffering.

Great houses crumble to powder, bleak and black,
Places I used to call home,
It all makes me cower.

Howls echoing, like a snake hissing in a cave,
"This isn't Allah's will!"
I wish I was so brave.

I'm injured and I think I'm mental,
No way I can escape this bleak, dull, war-torn city,
Is it even a city?

I'm frightened of the corpses
Sprinkled on the town like it's an ice cream,
I don't know the streets anymore,
Nor if my family exist,
I know the rage of war and the grimace of extreme
Won't ever change.

What did I do to be surrounded by war?
What did I do to be enclosed by hate?

Shouldn't we be the same?
We're humans after all
And humans are ugly and vile.

Katherine Cross (12)
Great Sankey High School, Great Sankey

Me And You

Pools of green and seas of blue,
You and me, me and you,
Eyes that shine like the moon and stars,
Hoping and dreaming, the universe is ours.

Curls of blonde and braids of red,
When you're gone, my world is dead,
But, then, you return and my sadness disappears,
As being alone was once something to fear.

We are alike in every way,
We stay together through long school days,
We both like cats,
We both like Friends and we stay together until the end.

Pools of green and seas of blue,
You and me, me and you.

Each time you smile, another star appears in the sky,
Each time you laugh, the sun shines a little brighter,
But nothing describes how great it feels being your friend.

Ruby Conchie (11)
Great Sankey High School, Great Sankey

Eyes Of A Slave

I'm waiting for tomorrow,
But scared tomorrow will never come,
My last sight is upon my heels
And I'm scared for my heart as it runs,
Hours are still to come
And, now, we're in the day,
The time is finally here,
But, now, I look away,
Days, weeks, months, years appear,
I now gaze into the future,
As though it's meant to be,
Always looking for the day I can be happy,
I spend too much time looking forward,
As I'm cleaning, I'm becoming blind,
Since you don't see what I have left behind,
Now, I know,
The only happiness I have
Is the happiness of love inside.

Lybah Ahmed (12)
Great Sankey High School, Great Sankey

A Little Message

The girl with the smile
Has been hurting for a while,
Trying to keep her tears inside
But struggling as she finds a friend.

People walk up to her as she gets her hopes up,
But realises they only came to give her bad luck,
She doesn't want to be alone,
But is still unknown.

After school, she always sits on the kerb,
Waiting for someone to help her,
But that's just a dream for her.

Scared to walk up to her house at night,
She doesn't want them to know she has no light inside.

It was then, one day,
She had enough
And
Gave up.

Keira Davies (11)
Great Sankey High School, Great Sankey

Pineapple On A Pizza

"Try this slice of pizza!"
Said my aunty Lisa,
She handed me a piece,
I wanted to leave.

Who on earth puts pineapple on pizza?
This is the worst crime you can ever do!
Who created this, who?

"Pineapple on pizza!"
"Give it a try!"
"Goodbye!"

Pineapple on a pizza is horrible
And it seems too dull,
It is not worth a try,
It doesn't look good on the eye!

If you meet me, you know what I'll say,
Never try to eat it,
Just throw it away!

Madison Knowles (12)
Great Sankey High School, Great Sankey

You And Me

I see you all alone,
Waiting and watching,
The wooden bench withering away,
The light in your eyes, gone.

Walking through the crowded grounds
Where all the people are ghosts,
I was waiting for you,
I'll be waiting for you for eternity.

You and me were inseparable,
You and me were true love,
Now, I'm gone, you're dying,
Now, I'm gone, you're having mistrust.

You are now at my resting place,
You are now with me,
We are not together again,
You and me are home.

Gwen Springall (15)
Great Sankey High School, Great Sankey

Mental Health Awareness

If you believe you can't talk to anyone,
You're wrong!
If you believe nobody cares about you,
You're wrong!
If you believe you're invisible,
You're wrong!
If you believe you're alone,
You're wrong.
So, Britain, get talking
Because there are so many people to talk to.

Isabelle Grace Eastham (11)
Great Sankey High School, Great Sankey

Five Degrees Tonight

I met him by chance, he said, "I know you've got a man,
But give me your hand,"

They called him Cobain, we couldn't see his pain,
I begged him but he was not the same,
I could tell what he wanted, all he wanted was to be sane,
Broken heart on his cheek, he got all the blame.

Broken man,
Sitting on the floor behind the bus,
Tears dampening his friend's cuff,
All we wanted was for him to be tough,
Little did we know, the tough guy act was a bluff.

Tears rolled down my cheeks,
I couldn't even peek,
Rest in Peace Lil' Peep.

Aliesha Smith (14)
Haringey Tuition Service, Tottenham

The Fireman

Blazing infernos billowing smoke,
Towering upwards into the blackening sky,
The crackling belongings burning to ash,
Filling the ears of onlookers,
Bells ringing,
Parents screaming,
People weeping,
Singed by fire,
No escaping,
Forever burning.

Sam Bardner (16)
Haringey Tuition Service, Tottenham

Neglect As A Singer

On stage, there is me,
Singing like I'm meant to be free,
But there's something different
About pop star life.

On the stage, I'm a fragile girl
Who only likes to twirl,
Off the stage, no one knows me
As a neglected, sad little freak.

No one knows what life's really like,
I had never learned to ride a bike
Or even gone to the county fair
Where everyone had a flair.

I was different from other kids
And made lots of bids,
I would sit and think about my life
And I knew my dad didn't need a wife.

At one point, I wanted to commit suicide,
But I wasn't ready to die,
Like many other pop stars who didn't cope,
I just needed to hope.

I didn't get to ride a bike
Or even stay the night,
I didn't go to the county fair,
That was the one thing I couldn't bear.

I can't handle any more neglect,
This is an effect,
For anyone in the world,
This is me, a young girl.

Ella Wakefield (11)

Lynn Grove Academy, Gorleston-on-Sea

100,000 Eyes Staring

I stand backstage breathing
As if I'm entering the lion's den,
My hands shaking like mad,
Wanting a hug from my dad, Ken.
I think, *I'm only seventeen,*
I can't do this, I'm mad!
But then I remember
If I don't do this my family will be sad.
A man walks up to me and says,
"Are you ready to go?"
My brain is saying yes
But my heart is saying no.
But I have to go with my brain,
It's the only thing that's keeping me sane,
So I start walking
As if I were on ice,
But just remember,
You have to be nice,
So I get on stage
With eyes locked on me,
But luckily the lights
Are blocking all I can see,
So I take a deep breath
And let my lungs do the rest.

Livvy Francis Ellen Grady (11)
Lynn Grove Academy, Gorleston-on-Sea

Flashbacks

Lights! Flashing!
Armed men were running through my house,
Police dogs sniffing every corner,
I was screaming, shouting,
My children were crying and hiding in corners,
The sirens echoed through my head like a song on replay.

I was in the consulting room,
My children were in a care home,
A camera in the corner of the room,
They had found the drugs,
A sudden chill ran through my body
My heart beating like a drum.

Everywhere I look, I see walls,
I'm trapped, I feel like a caged animal,
My knuckles are in agony because this place is testing my patience,
Every minute, torture,
My children call every day, asking, "When's Daddy coming home?"

These flashbacks in my memory,
It's been five years.

Harriet Collingwood (12)
Lynn Grove Academy, Gorleston-on-Sea

Slavery

Slavery,
Slavery,
Slavery.

Each day I'm abused and beat,
Lost for years, I haven't eaten meat,
So many scars but all the same story,
Need to escape this mess so dark and gory.

Slavery,
Slavery,
Slavery.

As I grow my body turns to lead,
It'll make no difference when I'm dead,
Every day is the same brutal day,
Dark, hurtful and grey.

Slavery,
Slavery,
Slavery.

Next generation, you're reading this,
Stop slavery, there are too many risks,
It's coming to the time where I will pass,
It will end slowly and harsh.

Slavery,
Slavery,
Slavery.

I was a part of
And hope not to look down on
Slavery.

Lauren Louise Kingsley (12)
Lynn Grove Academy, Gorleston-on-Sea

I'm Sid The Sloth

Yes, I'm Sid the sloth,
I'm not one to use a cloth,
I don't like this thing called cleaning,
If I'm honest, it has no meaning.

I snooze for fifteen hours per day,
That leaves only nine hours to play,
At night I sneak around to eat
The lovely hibiscus and leaves.

Although I have a fun time to play,
I still have to worry about my day,
I sit and wonder if this will be my last
All those fun and games in the past.

My lovely rainforest at risk,
But all the humans do is listen to their music discs,
They love causing deforestation
For our wonderful sloth population.

They will leave us with no shelter or food,
We will have to get them sued.

Jessica Davies (12)
Lynn Grove Academy, Gorleston-on-Sea

Mr Poverty

I ain't no Mr Rich,
I ain't no diamond galore,
I ain't no Mr Medic
With an ointment for every sore.

I ain't no Mr Wise
With an answer to every question,
I ain't no Mr Helpful,
With every idea, a great suggestion!

I ain't no Mr Brave,
The one that wears the cape,
I ain't no Mr Sly
With a trick for every escape.

I am Mr Poverty, living on the streets,
A simple beggar, eating whatever treats,
I don't laugh, I don't smile,
I haven't joked in a while.

It is not fun in the winter,
I have to put up with an infected splinter,
I am Mr Poverty,
I am Mr Poverty
And Mr Poverty is me...

Dallas Eley (13)
Lynn Grove Academy, Gorleston-on-Sea

Bombs Break Through

The day has begun peacefully,
I'm lying in bed with a lovely cup of tea.
"What was that sound?"
I can hear people screaming and footsteps stomping,
My house shook but now stands still,
I look out of my window but no more is to be seen,
I think, *I'll go back to enjoy my cup of tea!*
But I don't get much time for that as it happens again,
This time I see what is happening,
So I ricochet for shelter
But before I know it, my house is gone,
My walls and everything, just gone!
Then something happens in just one push of a trigger,
There I am in those soggy trenches and trigger after trigger,
More people come and go,
This is my life now!

Kumani Debbage (12)

Lynn Grove Academy, Gorleston-on-Sea

Approval

It's uploaded into the sky,
Now everybody can see it,
I am now online,
The world can now see my flaws.

The comments fall in like a waterfall,
All of the heartless, negative people
Flood the post with their unnecessary words,
I am sat here, hopelessly hoping for someone's approval,
I will wait and wait...

My self-esteem is like ink in your pen,
Always going down,
But every now and then I get a top-up
With a tiny bit of kindness,
But once something horrible is said,
It's always stuck there,
Never disappearing.

I will wait and wait,
Until I am approved as beautiful,
I will have to carry on hoping.

Amber Butcher (13)
Lynn Grove Academy, Gorleston-on-Sea

A Singer's Perspective

As I come out onto the bright stage,
The pounding of my heart is on full-speed,
There are two voices in my head.
One, *you can do this.*
Two, *don't mess up.*
As I start to let my voice rip,
All I see are cheering people
And in comes the third voice inside my head,
You can't do this.

I speed out of the brightly-coloured stage,
All I can see in my mind
Are posts of people angry
And giving shade about me.
But people make mistakes every day,
So what's wrong when I make one?
If this is how people see me
Then I am going to show them
What it's like to be me!

Emmi-Louise Nichols (11)
Lynn Grove Academy, Gorleston-on-Sea

Hour-Long Minutes

Every minute seems like an hour,
I have no money, freedom or power,
Life is rough, living is tough,
I'm gradually rotting away.

I would love a small bit of money,
But people don't care and find me funny,
Life is bad, I am sad,
I'm gradually rotting away.

It's really cold, I would love some heat,
I'm freezing under my dirty sheet,
It's not hot, soon I'll rest,
I'm gradually rotting away.

My old hound, he is like my best friend,
Sticking together until near the end,
Please send food, even chewed,
I'm gradually rotting away.

Evan Howell (12)
Lynn Grove Academy, Gorleston-on-Sea

Menace Doggo

A cute little doggo,
Only two years of age
Will tear apart your house
Or your homework page.

When we adopted him,
I felt like I could fly,
He was so small and cute
And so fluffy, I wanted to die.

We took him home
At eight months of age,
We bought him some toys
And a brand-new cage.

As time passed by,
He was one year of age
And he was allowed to sleep,
Outside of his cage.

We bought him a cake
And lots of new toys,
The family was round
And he tore up all of his old toys!

Harrison Dack (12)
Lynn Grove Academy, Gorleston-on-Sea

You Can Do Anything

We made a team
When we were fourteen,
A bunch of other boys having fun.

Then we became professional,
It all changed,
Diets, workouts and much more,
It happened as quick as a cheetah.

The next year changed our lives,
We were in the Championship,
Scoring goals like it was nothing,
1-0, 2-0, 3-0, 4-0, 5-0.

We won the League,
Breaking records,
Now we are in the Premier League,
Six months passed and we were top of the League,
Another six months and we won the Premier League.

Finley Matthew Barnett (12)
Lynn Grove Academy, Gorleston-on-Sea

The Great Night

At Anfield, we're 3-0 down,
Six minutes in and it's 1-0 to us!
Divock Origi starts it up,
Big Shaq crosses to Gini,
2-0, now it's game on.

All of this happening in front of my eyes,
We are so close to this Anfield surprise!
Into the box and Gini puts it in,
I'm jumping with joy!
All we need is one more
On this great night.

It is now a corner,
I see Divock's free,
I tell Trent to cross it into the box,
Divock's second and our fourth
On this great night!

Jensen Durrant (13)
Lynn Grove Academy, Gorleston-on-Sea

Life As A Dancer

I am a dancer,
I am energetic,
I am happy,
I am stressed.

Being a dancer can be fun,
Apart from when you're about to perform,
The lights are ready,
So am I.

I always want to be on my feet
But my mum says I need to rest,
The big day has come,
I'm so scared.

I am ready
But very stressed,
Oh no,
It's almost my turn.

My number has been called,
My music is turned on,
I'm about to go on,
Wish me good luck!

Hallie Smith (11)
Lynn Grove Academy, Gorleston-on-Sea

I Am The Beggar

Every day I watch people pass by happily
With their families,
I sit and hope
With my arms stretched out wide.

I slowly run out of food and water,
Why will nobody help me?
I am like them,
Why do they keep ignoring me?

I'm scared, all alone in this big world,
My arms ache every minute of the day
From endlessly holding a cup that I use
To get something, anything that can help me in this scary
world.

Why will nobody help a homeless person in need?

Alex Atkins (12)
Lynn Grove Academy, Gorleston-on-Sea

Pretty Little Secrets

Being an astronaut is a lot of work,
I have no words to say except don't go,
If you do meet me there,
It's only good to share,
I have no friends here and no way home,
But I miss my family, I really do care,
But there is one thing I forgot to share,
I'm not alone here, there's more than two,
I'm scared to say it
Out into the world,
There we go,
We have aliens here too!

Khloe Nixon (12)
Lynn Grove Academy, Gorleston-on-Sea

The Words Of A Dying Turtle

Turtles are dying
From the plastic in the sea,
How has our planet
Come to be this polluted?
A whirlpool of death
From the plastic in the sea,
Save the turtles!

The oceans are swirling with plastic,
My friends in the sea are dying
All because of you,
Your use of plastic bottles and straws
Is going to kill me,
You're going to kill all of our kind,
Save the turtles!

Saisha Hill (11)
Lynn Grove Academy, Gorleston-on-Sea

Messi The GOAT

I am Lionel Messi,
One of the best,
I score more than the rest,
Me and my team, scoring the goals,
Always going between the poles,
I get a free kick, then I score,
Then the crowd gives a roar,
I am Lionel Messi.

I play for Barcelona,
I play for Argentina,
Argentina is my home town!

Marc Azevedo (12)
Lynn Grove Academy, Gorleston-on-Sea

Football But Sad

He's good, he's sad,
People say he's bad,
When he goes in public, he wears a hood,
Unwanted attention from fame.

He says it's lame
To have too much fame,
You can't do anything without being recognised,
"Give me a break!"
Unwanted attention from fame.

George Seaman (11)
Lynn Grove Academy, Gorleston-on-Sea

Through The Eyes Of A Monkey

I am swinging in my cage,
My long arms swoop from side to side,
I run fast after my friends,
I am picking and eating
The leaves off the tree,
I am climbing the cage
In front of the four people watching,
I am happy!
The sun is out,
I am a monkey!

William Arthur Hodds (11)
Lynn Grove Academy, Gorleston-on-Sea

Fortnite

I start in the Battle Bus
And it is such a fuss,
I jump to glide,
I nearly died,
I land at Pleasant Park,
Then hit a tree with bark,
Then I look up
And suit up.
I am ready for a journey,
Then I kill a guy named Burnie,
He was a bot,
I ate a chilli, boy was it hot!
Then I ran and got another hit,
This guy, however, was named Bill,
I reached the top twenty
With two kills, now that isn't plenty,
I am goaded on the stick,
The next person I kill is named Nick,
I snipe another kid,
His name was Sid,
An RPG hits my base!
Against the storm, I will race,
I get a bit low, so I will bandage,
Another kill I get, I'm on a rampage,
I reach top ten,
There's another kill, his name was Ben,

I hit him with a boogie bomb,
That was the end of Tom,
I am top five,
How did I survive?
Beaming with my scar,
I will get very far!
A death to a noob,
This time, it was Ruby Rude,
A beam with the AR gets another kill,
This time their name was Jill,
Nine kills now,
It is safe to say I could take a bow,
I pop a ninety,
It looks quite mighty,
We get into a build battle,
I take the high ground,
He then frowned,
I hit him with a pump, it is a big bash,
Then I turn on my mic and say he's trash.

Jack Petrozzi (12)
Ormiston Horizon Academy, Tunstall

When Will I Be Bought?

They stare into my brown button eyes
But then they walk away.
They walk into that other aisle,
The one that leads to my dismay.

The one that's full of games
And electronics galore,
No matter how many hours they get,
They always want more.

But you can't cuddle a PlayStation,
You can't have tea with Mario
But apparently children don't need us,
So I guess we'll have to go.

So now I just sit here
Collecting dust and dirt.
Wondering when I'll be bought,
Me in my blue shirt.

But then it happens,
It happens so fast.
That little girl,
I've seen her in the past.

She asked her mum for me
But she said no
And now she's back,
I better put on a show!

I widen my smile,
She catches my eye
She stands on her tiptoes
My, oh my.

It finally happened,
I have been bought!
I hope you understand,
The lesson that's being taught.

You don't need games,
Electronics galore.
You have us,
Do you need much more?

Hayley Rachel Hughes (13)
Ormiston Horizon Academy, Tunstall

Life Of A Football

The keeper collects me from the stands,
Slams me on the floor,
I'm dying of pain,
I get played out to the centre backs.
He kicked me hard,
My body is in pain.
I'm still here for seventy minutes.
I get played over the top to Ronaldo,
He keeps running with me,
I hit the crossbar.
Suddenly, I'm dizzy,
Where am I?
I hear the cheers of fans, I think I'm in the goal.
It comes back to me, I see them celebrating.
I hear the commentator,
He said, "Fabulous strike,
Ryan Boot had no chance,
Vale was down by one."
I hear the whistle for half-time.
Michael Owen, the guest referee,
He put me down gently
And I live.
Tom Pope starts off the game,
He shoots and I'm in the goal,
I can't go on any longer, I'm dying.
It's the final play,

Ryan Boot is up,
I'm whipped into the box.
He bicycle kicks me and Vale win.
I'm glad it's over,
I'm in so much pain.

Tom Tinsley (13)
Ormiston Horizon Academy, Tunstall

War O' War, Why O' Why?

I lived a normal life
'Til I turned nineteen,
When my whole life was turned upside down,
Something dangerous happened in Bosnia,
That was all we knew,
As we marched into battle, totally blind,
The experience was like no other,
The trauma and the heartbreak,
The bitterness and the cold,
This sort of thing tears into your soul,
I've stood helpless,
Watching people die,
Wondering how I'm still alive,
Then, one day, everything changed,
I woke up just like usual,
Took up my place along the line,
Looking out across no-man's-land,
Barbed wire, corpses and mud,
One hell of a lot of mud,
Was all the eye could see,
Then something happened,
Only God knows what,
I felt a sharp pain in my head,
It was agony,
Then something strange happened,
Everything went black,

I heard a shout,
"Oh, Lord, help!" it said,
Was this the end?

Tom Smith (11)
Ormiston Horizon Academy, Tunstall

Bullying

I walked away,
I watched the teachers shake their heads in dismay,
I felt so alone,
Nobody believed me at home,
Who else can I tell?
Where do I go?

It went on and on all the time,
Why couldn't bullying be a crime?
The way they made me feel,
Disgusted, abandoned,
But they never got blamed.

Little things, too stupid to tell,
But it all gets on top of me,
Even just two words,
"You smell!"

The way I feel is hard to describe,
Apart from dejected and small inside,
Often I see a knife and think of what I could do,
But that little voice inside me says,
No, this isn't you.

I will never be normal again,
My happiness is running out,
Like ink on a pen,

My sadness breaks the scale,
Flying straight over ten.

So, if you are being bullied,
Speak out today,
Don't end up like me,
Alone in dismay.

Morgan Corcoran (12)
Ormiston Horizon Academy, Tunstall

Weather

As I walked through the field,
on an early morning stretch,
the sun shone brightly from out
of the clouds.
My feet graciously swept through
the summer grass,
which was blowing strongly into
the direction of the hushing gust of wind.
I continued to walk,
rain slowly started to drip,
drip down my face.
Faster and faster.
The rain began to fall faster
until loud, harsh grumbles
like a large giant burst out of the sky.
Suddenly, silver streaks of lightning
struck loudly in the air.
The field had nearly come to an end
but then, large crystal-white crystals
began to fall from the sky.
As they began to fall,
heavier and heavier,
a thin white blanket appeared on the floor.
The field came to an end.
I was home,
comfy with the fire on

as the snow gently, graciously,
fell beside me.

Ella Louise Mae Daniels (14)

Ormiston Horizon Academy, Tunstall

Football

I was taken off the shelf,
I finally had an owner.
The soft, sharp grass saved my fall.
It was like landing on a pillow.
I bounced to the soft, swaying clouds.
I was kicked across the garden,
over and over.
But it went dark and the night began.

The sun shone
and the clouds went out of sight
but it was the worst time of my life.
"Nooo!"
I heard the kids scream as I flew
into the unknown.

I landed behind the fence,
I smashed against the tree.
I knew there wasn't a way out.
I deflated like a popped balloon.
As sadness filled me,
days passed, months passed,
years passed.

I was like a lone wolf,
living on my own behind the fence.
Fifteen years later, I saw something,
it was him.

All grown up but he came back
He actually came back.

Jack Pye (13)
Ormiston Horizon Academy, Tunstall

Patting Paws

I can't believe my ears,
The roaring of the lion-like dogs,
My glazed eyes swell with tears,
The cheering humans clog my senses.

My patting paws
Making my feet go sore,
Running on raw adrenaline,
I leap into a shallow bush,
I crash into the ground,
My heart pounding,
The hounds howling,
Aggressive growling.

The towering beasts,
Their bloody, sharp as dagger teeth,
I manage to slither away,
"It's okay, it's okay, it's okay,"
They want me to obey,
They prance out from the bushes raging,
The humans sneak behind me and shove me into a tiny
cage.

They cheer and rattle me about,
I hit my shoulder,
I am knocked out cold,
My torn shoulder blinds me with pain.

I try to be tame,
Only I remain.

It's not okay.

Christianne Lawton (14)
Ormiston Horizon Academy, Tunstall

Anxiety

I say I'm fine
When I'm really not,
There's no way to describe it,
My tongue's in a knot.

I wake up every morning,
Feeling the same way,
Like I'm drowning
And there's no escape.

I constantly feel
Like I've done something wrong,
I'm losing myself,
I don't belong.

My mind is racing,
My palms are sweaty,
My body's shaking,
My heart won't slow.

It's like swimming in the ocean
With no land in sight,
I'm slowly dying,
I'm not alright.

I know what to say,
But I can't put it into words,
My mind's growing grey,
Am I even me anymore?

It's taking over my brain,
I can't run, I can't hide,
It's seeping through my veins,
I wish I hadn't lied.

Holly Maltby (13)
Ormiston Horizon Academy, Tunstall

Life Of A Corkey

The bowler stood at his mark,
He rubbed half of my body against him,
Then he began to run.
He jumped and bowled.
I flew through the air at 90mph,
I hit the bat and flew to the boundary.
Four runs signalled the umpire.

I lay on the floor,
By myself, all alone.
A fielder picked me up,
Spat on me, rubbed me.
Then lobbed me into the bowler's hands
He ran up again and bowls
The batsman missed.
I smacked into the middle stump
And sent the bails flying.
The crowd erupted.
One more wicket to go.

He rubbed me against his white outfit.
Ran up again
And bowled.
I flew straight,
Hit the bat
Straight for a six but I didn't stop.
I bounced straight into a car,

I smashed into the car and broke the window.
That was my life, what about you?

Oliver Wootton (13)
Ormiston Horizon Academy, Tunstall

I Am A Human Being!

Why can't I be normal?
Why can't I be me without being judged?
Why can't I go without being stared at?
Why can't people just understand I am a human being?
I am someone's daughter, lover and friend,
I can't control my emotions,
I can't control the voices,
I can't control what I do,
Why can't people understand I am normal?
I am me, I don't need fixing
Because I am not broken,
I feel isolated,
The pills make me feel numb and violated,
I am expected to take my pills,
Day in, day out,
But what if I don't want to?
What if, one day, I want to feel free?
Want to be me for a day?
Society expects me to be normal,
A robot that goes along with the world,
That fills society's needs,
I want to be me.
I am a human being!

Georgia Simcock (13)
Ormiston Horizon Academy, Tunstall

Being A Teen (Bullying)

Bullying is hard,
You feel like you are alone,
You don't want to get up in the morning,
Or go to class,
I feel scared,
I don't talk to my family much anymore,
I don't feel safe anymore, or happy,
You feel depressed,
You end up going to therapy,
But nothing changes,
You just say it's okay,
It's all lies,
Lies that everyone believes,
But, inside, it's a whole new world,
I don't even play in the street anymore,
Every day you get bullied in school,
Even online,
There's no escape,
No matter what,
All you want to do is sleep
And never wake up again,
I do, I'm sick of it,
What have I done to deserve this?
Everyone says it's a part of life,
But it shouldn't be.

Freya Howle (12)
Ormiston Horizon Academy, Tunstall

Captive

I'm just here, stuck in the zoo,
The reason that I'm here starts with *you.*
In the night, the other animals call out to each other,
But then there's me, I'm missing my mother.

How will I get out of here?
Everyone just comes by and peers.
I just want to get out
But I'll get tortured if I shout.

What am I going to do?
Well, all of that starts with you.
You were the one that put me here
And now my home is far from near.

There is never any space,
It's like my life just goes to waste
It's horrible in here
And my mother's whereabouts is what I fear.

You can make a change,
Starting by getting me out o this cage.
Just set me free and leave me be.
Thank you.

Jacob Keeling (14)
Ormiston Horizon Academy, Tunstall

Kylie Skin

As Stormi was making a storm,
I was thinking about my glamorous Gucci,
Today was Kylie Skin and it was gonna kill it,

I had to stock up on my sister's snatched lip fillers
Before the brilliant, bomb launch,

As my maids made me my marvellous lunch,
I looked on my feed and everyone loved it,
I was shimmering and shining while I was dining,
But the clock clicked while I crept upstairs,

My make-up had to look miraculous,
Magnificent like a magical mermaid,
But wait! I was worried about the time
I was about to cry
I didn't have enough time to do my make-up

I washed my whole face,
I was gonna be late,
But whatever the weather,
I will be late like a loony.

Maisy Garside (12)
Ormiston Horizon Academy, Tunstall

Alone

Imagine how alone I would feel,
If I had no one to go to
Or had nowhere to cry,
Being down all the time,
Having no one around.
To guide me through the difficult times,
Without me cutting any lines.

Going out on walks to clear my head
Getting lost on the way.

But what if it's too late,
What if I'm already gone
By the time you're actually bothered.

What if I'd already cut lines?
If I'd been alone all my life
Having no one to run to
Or nowhere to cry.

The person I only want, cares
They care but I'm guilty
For placing all my problems on them
Just because I can't help myself.

So I'd rather stay alone.

Mia Reese Wallace (14)
Ormiston Horizon Academy, Tunstall

Answer

Fear.
Pure and unbidden terror,
Running like wildfire,
Leaving behind a ghostly grin,
Reaching out to all creatures,
Twisting their senses, and
Calm state of mind.

Screams.
Aimless in the ascent of air,
Motionless. Void of awareness
Fragments of metal shoot in every direction,
Now, like corpses, asleep upon the ground,
Glass lies shattered, unsolvable
Jigsaw puzzles coating the road.

In silent sleep with a thousand sisters and brothers,
I hear Death's motherly call to return,
Amidst the boundless and bare, stretching life,
My eyes, dull with the dreaded fear
Of death. My long acquainted friend.
Alone, we meet with bitter rejoice.
The call is answered.

Jessica Thompson (15)
Ormiston Horizon Academy, Tunstall

I Say That I'm Okay

I say that I'm okay,
But my brain can't take the pain,
The words that you say,
They don't make sense anymore,
I feel like everyone's out to get me,
I don't feel safe anymore.

I say that I'm okay,
But it hurts me inside,
The way you stare at me
And the way they laugh and point,
I feel like I'm a monster,
I don't feel normal anymore.

I say that I'm okay,
But I can't lie anymore,
The things people say,
They will never understand,
I feel like I'm alone,
I don't feel happy anymore.

I say that I'm okay,
But this time I really am,
My name is Lisa Andrews
And I have mental health.

Emma Davis (12)
Ormiston Horizon Academy, Tunstall

The Apple

As the wind blows
as the large apple tree waves,
this place is tranquil,
it is a place of peace.

The beautiful sun docks on the horizon
it reflects a warm light on the ponds of the water
It shines throughout this forest of delight.

As I sit on the treetops
I take my time to admire this world of wonder.

Then what I've been waiting for,
the pickers.
They pick me up from the highest treetop,
they pull me down by my stem
and put me in a pen.

As I drive down to the large, noisy supermarket,
I am placed in a cart
with thousands of others.

I wait as my life goes by
and soon enough I am turned into an apple pie.

William Anthony Vousden (12)
Ormiston Horizon Academy, Tunstall

Smelly Feet

I am a shoe
And I am worn by you,
Oh, how your feet stink,
I wish that I would shrink.

Can you please take me off today?
Please, just throw me away!
Can you give me to someone else?
Because your feet really smell!

Your feet are ever so smelly,
I would rather be a welly,
Never mind, the feet would be even more smelly,
Can I just be some jelly?

I just can't wait until the day,
The day that you throw me away,
I just can't wait until that day
Because it makes me feel a special sort of way.

Finally, here I am on the floor
And you don't use me anymore.
Here you come with a bin,
I will take that as a win...

Tom Walker (15)
Ormiston Horizon Academy, Tunstall

Bully!

I flicked through my phone,
Messaging my friends
Waiting for my tea to be done.

I put my phone down on the table
And a message popped up on my phone,
Saying nasty things...
'You're fat', 'You're ugly', 'You deserve to die'.
I wasn't expecting it...

I didn't want to say to my family
She kept texting me all night
That I didn't have any sleep.
I couldn't go to school today
I'd have to make myself sick!

I was scared that she'd be at school
All day I got texts
And still didn't tell anyone.
Why is this getting on my mind?

Lexi Glover (11)
Ormiston Horizon Academy, Tunstall

Football

You never touch me with bare hands.
You always kick me with your sharp boots.
You make me fly across a field.
Yet, what did I do to you?

You kick and throw me at walls.
You place me in a dark room
And if my skin stars to peel,
You throw me in the bin!

After I have helped you get better at football,
And got you through your first match,
And your first shot,

But every time we come home,
I just sit with the football boots.

Now I am old and I have grown my first hole
And my fair share of looks
I am just a useless football,
That will never be seen again.

Faith Stubbs (13)
Ormiston Horizon Academy, Tunstall

A Paramedic's Job

My life was going to change in about forty-five minutes,
I had been called up to a job,
My radio screaming and shouting for more paramedics,
My heart started to beat faster,
A sudden bang came from my radio,
I had to make a choice, a quick one.
Second after second, I knew lives were in my hands,
Reaching speeds of seventy miles per hour,
Concentration beaming from my face.
A car came out of a junction without seeing me
And the wet wheels on my ambulance
Slipped into the side of the car.
"Are you alright?"
Shouting from a woman,
Bleeding out of my head,
There was no going back.

Owen Shuter (12)
Ormiston Horizon Academy, Tunstall

Glory

So much blood, so much shouting
The emperor raised his glass,
Whilst the crowd continued chanting
Along the walls a head would smash.

"Pugna non-perfecta est!"
A black figure emerged from the dark
This was not a time to rest
A Samurai concealed behind armour of bark

I was intimidated by his curvature
His kanabo dragged across the bloody sand
However, I was no amateur
I'd ever seen anything of a size so grand.

The dash of steel on steel grew loud
His eyes struck me with fear
I heard nothing but the roar of the crow
My death would be from that sound.

Cameron Dawson (13)
Ormiston Horizon Academy, Tunstall

Nan Like You!

God looked down at his garden and saw you shining,
He takes the best people, I don't know why.
I love you, Nan, but he took you away from me,
Great nans, just like you, go unexpectedly,
I don't know why.
When Saturday came, I jumped in the air,
Couldn't wait to get down to your house,
Love was everywhere.
I miss you so much.
When it's time to go, the feel of your cheek against my lips.
When I need your advice, you gave me tips.
I miss you as much as I love you,
I wish I could tell you how much I love you.
Love you, I care,
See you when I get there.

Tayla-Louise Kinsey (11)
Ormiston Horizon Academy, Tunstall

A Pineapple Pizza

I was having a party in the freezer
When somebody thought they would have a pizza,
They picked me up, opened the packaging
And swiped my pineapple away.

I felt like my life had ended,
If they wanted a pizza without pineapple,
Why did they choose me?

I sat in the oven
Whilst being cooked,
But, instead of puffing up to my glory,
I sat there and did nothing but think,
I came out of the oven
And saw a pair of eyes, staring down at me.

The next thing I knew,
I was in the bin with my pineapple,
I was finally returned to my former glory.

Keira Colclough (13)
Ormiston Horizon Academy, Tunstall

The Huntings

Another day I hide in the shadows,
Another day I watch one of my family die,
I feel scared and lonely
and I hate hiding from them.
They chase me down
and kill my family.
Every night I cry by myself,
hoping my tears would wash away from the pain
but it doesn't, it only makes it hurt more.
I try to be brave,
but it never works,
I just want to be able to run free,
run away from the problems,
run away from everything.
They use my teeth for jewellery,
they use my fur for decoration
and leave me with my rotting body,
frightened and scared.

Grace Ainsworth (13)
Ormiston Horizon Academy, Tunstall

Airpods

I was all wrapped up,
Waiting for a new owner.
I lay in my plastic bed,
I was a loner.

A young boy came into the shop,
Then he said hello.
He paid the money to the man
When I was unwrapped I wasn't yellow

Little did he know the truth,
I wasn't living for long.
But I kept him happy
But buying me was wrong.

My time had finally come,
My owner was really low.
But he stood up strong
And knew I had to go.

To stay happy,
He bought a new pair.
Thanks for reading this,
Our poem ends there.

Rehan Abbas Malik (12)
Ormiston Horizon Academy, Tunstall

Feminist

I treat people equally,
girls and boys have their own rights
I am a feminist
I want to make
things right,
I tried so hard to get
it right.
Now look at me,
famous and proud,
I make people happy,
I like to help.

My life is amazing,
it took me
years to get to this
stage,
I played Hermione in
Harry Potter,
my friends helped
me.
People call me a hero
because of what I did,
they love me.
Now,
let's go onto Beauty and the Beast,
he took my dad away from me
and then he was forgiven.

Demi-Leigh Davis (13)
Ormiston Horizon Academy, Tunstall

Dopey

I trip over stumps
and the littlest of lumps.
Even over my feet
what a little treat.

I'm loved by Snow White,
apparently, I'm a delight.
Even though I never help
because I always have to yelp.

I love blowing bubbles
and having lots of cuddles.
The rest are so serious
however, I'm just curious.

The animals are everywhere
going crazy over there.
Where is she?
Not with me.

I can see what's going on
Why has she been taken?
Will he save her?
If not, I'll be alone forever.

Megan Lowndes (15)
Ormiston Horizon Academy, Tunstall

Don't Fly, Soar!

My big ears flap in the wind,
I look down at the astonished crowds,
I'm doing this for my mum!
I have big ears,
I am proud,
I don't care what they think,
The clowns looking at me,
Elephants cheer,
The one, the only flying elephant.

I can see the magic in children's eyes,
They don't want to say their goodbyes.
I like the circus
And to eat citrus.
My treats are like peanuts,
I don't want to hear their tuts,
I love my ears,
I hear their cheers,
For the only, the only flying elephant,
Dumbo.

Lily-Rose Moreton
Ormiston Horizon Academy, Tunstall

Cries Of A Child

Every step I take
It's like every moment I could break.
A walk across town, it's no longer the same,
But more like a walk in a battlefield
of shame.

As I sit on the step by the maple tree.
The cries of a child overwhelm me.
As I look across the narrow lane,
I see the face of an innocent child.
As tears of sorrow roll down her face.
Her eyes show no hope but more fear,
For this incompetent place.

She should be running,
With laughter filling her face,
But she is crying in sorrow,
At the sight of this place.

Ella Amelia Hughes (13)
Ormiston Horizon Academy, Tunstall

Once...

Once I had dreams.
Once I was willing to come to school,
Now I skip,
Every day you ask me
"Are you okay?"
I say yes.

Once I had friends,
Once we used to play together,
Now I have none,
Rumours spread fast,
I soon learnt that I wasn't okay.

Once I was bullied,
Once it wouldn't stop,
Now I hide,
I hide away,
Start doing bad in class.

Once one person decided to stick up for me,
Once we got on forever,
Now I know I am okay,
I now can finally say,
"I'm okay!"

Olivia Rose Russell (13)
Ormiston Horizon Academy, Tunstall

Save The Turtles

We turtles are in danger,
We don't know what to do,
We need to keep being safer,
Us turtles need help now,
We are kept in captivity,
We need an activity,
Our relatives and children are dying,
Please help us so we stop crying.

All we are asking for is help,
It's not like we're asking for help,
We beg you to save us,
Our world is falling to pieces,
If you don't help then we will die,
I'm sure you don't want that,
We're sad that you don't care,
We do not bite,
Come and help,
We are turtles,
We are in danger!

Laura Edwards (11)
Ormiston Horizon Academy, Tunstall

Searching For A Master

My stomach gurgles,
Up there I sit.

Each day goes by.
My time ticks on.
The rules are quite simple.
Just rub me and wish.

You only have three,
So make them count,
As long as you remember,
I'm only a lamp.

Inside lives the Genie,
He's always by my side.
Forever in my heart,
Until the day we die.

It's not that easy,
You have to get me first
But don't get tempted,
I might live in gold,
But the second you touch it,
We will all explode!

Jemma Gaitley (13)
Ormiston Horizon Academy, Tunstall

I Stayed Strong

They kick
They punch
They never seem to have enough
They stare
They laugh
And they act really tough.

They judge all day
And text all night
Treat me like clay
In the morning
Light.

They think they can
Shape me
But I've had enough
I pushed them back
Came for attack
They shouted
They snarled
But it got worse from there.

I called for help
They got in trouble
I stayed strong
Didn't end my life
Because everyone

Deserves to
Fly.

Summer Burton (11)
Ormiston Horizon Academy, Tunstall

Green Highlighter

I am a highlighter,
pastel as can be,
part of a group
as green as a tree.

Me and the colours understand,
what it's like to be held,
by a human hand.

I'm only wanted during the day,
used to highlight essays, schoolwork,
maybe even lines in a play.

When night comes around,
I am forgotten,
trapped in a pencil case,
left to feel rotten.

So care for your highlighters,
let them feel free,
use them more often,
so they aren't sad like me.

Emily Landers (14)
Ormiston Horizon Academy, Tunstall

Animals In Cages (Zoo)

I'm in a cage, trapped for life
This is not fair, I have a life despite
I'm trapped in this prison for your entertainment
I want to be out with my family, what a shame it is.

I can move left and right but not very far
I'm trapped here behind these metal bars.
I don't like it here, I don't like this zone
I am so, so sad that I'm forced to call this home.

Please let us out, we don't want to be here
You might be scared but we're the one with more fear.

Max Waltho (14)
Ormiston Horizon Academy, Tunstall

Man's Best Friend

If in my world it's been seven years,
And in the human world, it's been one year,
How old would I be?

When I get left alone,
In the house,
There's no one but me!

I hate not getting attention,
I hate having too much,
I just want to feel free!

When my family come home,
I'm no longer alone
And them I'm on the throne!

Sometimes the living room door gets closed,
Sometimes it doesn't
And when it's not closed, I tend to pose!

Anya Shelley
Ormiston Horizon Academy, Tunstall

The Lost Alien

I am an alien and this is my story,
I was trying to get to Earth but they didn't want me,
I was not only angry but I was lonely,
I couldn't speak English but I tried,
They wouldn't let me into Earth,
But that wouldn't stop me,
I went back multiple times,
Only to get instant rejection,
I gave up, it was all over, goodbye Earth,
But I couldn't give up,
I learnt and got taught languages,
Then I went back,
I got in!
I got a job,
I lived a life.

Lewis Willatt (12)
Ormiston Horizon Academy, Tunstall

I'm A Ruler

I'm a ruler,
You can measure with me,
Draw lines with me
Or even use me as a sword.

I'm a ruler,
You can flick me,
Pick me up and throw me,
But don't make my nightmare true.

I'm a ruler,
My worst fear is turning into two,
But that fear soon came true,
Ouch!

I'm a sharp piece of glass,
The teacher is carrying me,
She's tossing me in the bin,
Well, I guess I'll live my life as garbage.

I'm trash.

Elliot Sharman
Ormiston Horizon Academy, Tunstall

Cheesecake

I am cold,
I am devoured,
I am appreciated,
I am never big enough,
I come in different flavours.
Lemon, I prefer,
The tin surrounds me.
I am not free.
My name is Jared
And I'm a cheesecake.

I change in temperature,
Defrosted as preferred,
People love to devour me,
I can be eaten by the sea,
Either way, it's best for me,
You can eat me as a millionaire,
No one can dislike my essence,
I am scrumptious,
And I am luscious.

Chloe Suzanne Smith (14)
Ormiston Horizon Academy, Tunstall

1929

The great war widows, underage assigning
and most importantly, the highway to the asylum
You have to be as brave as an arrow
and feel as light as a whisper as for you see
the man in white always has a place to be.
The barrier between me and she is more than to bear
but as I waited faithfully, someone visited,
there. Come, come, old friend, you,
never missed a shot, see if you miss,
I will be displeased and as I stand,
gun in hands, beware the guy,
is always behind.

Rhuben Robert Johnson (11)
Ormiston Horizon Academy, Tunstall

The Cookie Jar

Living in fear
watching the light.
If it comes any closer
I might die of fright.

The pain I felt
as they got torn apart.
Was nothing compared
to what was in my heart.

The cookie jar
is no longer a happy place.
Waiting in fear
of every child's face.

I became the only one left
I watched as they were taken
and put to rest
now I am standing
in the jar alone
a moment of silence
for the now broken home.

Kirsty Jones (15)
Ormiston Horizon Academy, Tunstall

Will I Ever Be Accepted?

I am trapped in my own mind,
Feeling like I can't escape this prison,
I get more lonely every second.
I feel suffocated like there is nowhere for me,
Breathe in these thoughts.
I can't fit in, worrying people will
Judge me for who I am.
Panic fills my mind before I do anything,
Is it good enough?
Will it make me look stupid?
Nothing can take this pain away.
I am alone in this word, no one will understand.
Why me? Why did I have to suffer?

Bryannah Barnett-Gibson (13)
Ormiston Horizon Academy, Tunstall

The True Fear As A Teen

Lying here, small and still,
Seeing my mother holding the pill,
My sister's eyes fill with tears,
All of them coming up in fear,
My five year younger sister slaps me across my nose,
I feel like all the doors to my future have been closed,
Hearing sirens coming at last,
My breathing feels like it's being cut off with a mask,
Now in the hospital bed,
Being all drugged up with meds,
Even though this is a true fear,
Part of this has got me here.

Lexi Ashmall (12)
Ormiston Horizon Academy, Tunstall

I Am A Pigeon

As the wind blows, I fly from tree to tree
But some people like me but many people don't.
But when they're people with guns
Fear comes out my eyes in case one day
I will get shot by a hunter.
When I am hungry, I eat bananas
They make me hyper but when I eat bird seeds and bread
I am bored.
Many people don't know what I am like!
I either poo on them or on their cars.
If I get seen in the dark, I could eat
Someone in two bites.

Jamal Winkle (11)
Ormiston Horizon Academy, Tunstall

True Emotions

Each day starts the same,
But it shouldn't be the same,
Fear is just an emotion,
Built-up from muffled feelings,
When the day ends, I feel scared again,
Loneliness is overpowering me
Nobody around to cry to,
So what am I supposed to do?
People come and go, so they will never know,
Time passes by,
Through the good and the bad,
But it all sticks with you
Like the night you never wished to have had,
This is who I am.

Amy Hansbury (14)
Ormiston Horizon Academy, Tunstall

Trigger

I'm being pointed,
My trigger about to be pulled,
Two children standing before me,
Alone, afraid,
Nowhere to go,
I don't want to hurt them,
But I have no choice.
The smirk on my owner's face,
Cold, heartless.

Screams of children fill the air
As they sit on the floor,
There is nothing I can do,
Then he counts down,
"Three, two, one..."

Bang!

He missed...

Shanice Mudzudza (12)
Ormiston Horizon Academy, Tunstall

Nelson Mandela's Feelings

The question is
What have I done?
Why do I deserve this?
Why do they hate black people?

That is what I think
In prison for being a coloured human being

Once I get out of here
I will bring white and black people together
To show that we black people have the same right as the
white population

Can I do it?
Every day I see the torture that black people are going
through
I just want it to end.

Tyler Jones (13)
Ormiston Horizon Academy, Tunstall

I Lay In A Lonely Field

W andering around a lonely field,
O ngoing gunshots I could hear,
R ationing for everyone that brought me a tear,
L ove was forgotten as I knew it was the end,
D ead people lay in a lonely field.

W ounded went off to nurses,
A lways I knew this place was filled with curses,
R egrets for leaving my family, I was dying in a lonely field.

Amelie Barlow (12)
Ormiston Horizon Academy, Tunstall

Cheese Vs Mouse

As I'm picked up and placed,
Upon the wooden board.
In front of me, I see the silver trap,
Waiting here, bored.

As time passes,
I finally see the small mouse approach.
Little does it know,
It's about to get a good crunching.

If I don't get munched,
The mouse will get crunched.
The mouse has no more to say
But at least I live another day.

Millie Williams
Ormiston Horizon Academy, Tunstall

Nowhere To Go

Standing here, on and off,
People come and go,
But not some.

Some have nowhere to go,
In the rain, in the snow.
As I bright up the night,

Keeping them warm so they can sleep tight,
Like the others, who had a chance
With a great, big house
And fancy cars and a nice, comfy bed.

But not some,
Because they have nowhere to go.

Leighton Nixon (12)
Ormiston Horizon Academy, Tunstall

Our Falling Animal Kingdom

Wildlife, what does it mean to our hearts?
Is it just a word without meaning?
Leave them like broken parts,
Dull rocks once gleaming.

Bluebells, once paint on a canvas, a blanket of blue,
Falling upon an ancient hue,
Names of heart and soul,
Running away like a mole.

Whales start to beach themselves,
Tortoiseshells tear away from their spines.

Grace Leigh (11)
Ormiston Horizon Academy, Tunstall

The Endangered Jaguar

As I crawl along the jungle floor,
Although I have just eaten, I want more,
Parrots, snakes or wild boars,
I don't care, I just want more, more, more!

My jet-black fur shining in the sun,
As I hear the fire of a gun,
My ears prick up at the sound
And I quickly turn around.

What the noise was, nobody knows,
Then my eyes start to close...

Mima Liv Parfitt (12)
Ormiston Horizon Academy, Tunstall

Elephant

E normous, gentle and kind
L ike I would ever hurt someone
E normous I seem on the outside but gentle inside
P oached I don't deserve that
H ydrating myself in the water
A bsolutely humongous ears I have
N ice, high leaves perfect for me to eat
T usks are my pride as I stride in my herd.

Lily Pomelli (14)
Ormiston Horizon Academy, Tunstall

Why Do People Bully?

Why do people bully?
Throughout my life this is
All the bullying I've seen...
One
A boy he was bullying another boy
Two
A girl in my old school was being mean to my friend
Bullying is wrong
Treat people the way
You want to be treated because
You probably wouldn't like it
If you got bullied
Please be kind.

Chloe Challinor (11)
Ormiston Horizon Academy, Tunstall

Lobby

L ittle bits of meat
O xo cubes
B low me because I'm hot
B ang me in the slow cooker
Y ou're going to love me

B read is dipped in my juice
R ead the newspaper
E at me because I'm juicy
A fter we're done, clean me up
D ickens is a good author.

Harry Ashton (14)
Ormiston Horizon Academy, Tunstall

The Perfect Two?

He holds my hand in his
I hold his hand in mine
Strolls through the park
And two glasses of wine.
Fancy dinners and takeaway nights
I help him with his struggles
And he helps me with mine.
Nothing but the perfect match
Except when we have our scraps
But nothing is perfect, don't you see
Everything ends eventually.

Alecia Ibinson (13)
Ormiston Horizon Academy, Tunstall

School As A Teacher

I see children running around the corridors each day,
At least twenty students come to my office each day,
Naughtier and naughtier each hour,
I wish I could lock them in a tower,
Behaviour points come in, one after the other,
It causes so much pain,
They need to get it inside their brains,
I need my bed,
Not the children inside my head.

Caitlyn Milward (12)
Ormiston Horizon Academy, Tunstall

Love And Hate

We love each other.
We hate each other
But nobody will ever hurt him.
He may be seventeen but I will always have his back.
If someone tried to beat him
I'd punch them in the back.
We fight, argue and say sorry after.
Nothing could ever stop my love for him,
We buy each other things for Christmas and birthday.

Kimberley Jane Meir (12)
Ormiston Horizon Academy, Tunstall

The Pear

Look at that human over there
His ugly face and ugly hair.

If you didn't know, I am a pear.
Oh no, he's coming to eat me!
Why did the shop owner sell me for free?

He's about to take a bite
Why do humans always eat me at night?
This isn't fair,
I am just a lonely, juicy pear.

Dylan Evans
Ormiston Horizon Academy, Tunstall

Marmite

I am a jar of Marmite
Normally I stay in a cupboard
Some people like me
Some people don't.
I can be bought in most shops.
So when they get home
They open me
And then they try me
The mum likes me
But the daughter doesn't
So they end up chucking
Me in the
Bin.

Inaya Jade Bromley (11)
Ormiston Horizon Academy, Tunstall

Save The Turtles

The plastic straws take my home,
My friends and my family.

Convert to metal or paper straws,
I pray.

Save my friend and save my family
Let me live, 'til I'm old, I pray.

Save me, please, stop polluting the oceans
Save them all, we're killing everyone slowly.

Evan Cameron Shallcross (12)
Ormiston Horizon Academy, Tunstall

The Adventures Of The Guinea Pig Called Deizle

I am the guinea pig who never likes to have anyone happy
or loud near me
My owner is nice but I hate how she always shouts, "Deizle!"
And I go running up as if she is giving me food, not that I
want it
I'm the cutest and the fluffiest in my family
I love my grumpy life and will never change.

Hannah Shingler (13)
Ormiston Horizon Academy, Tunstall

Tree Stumps

This was once one big forest,
Until that day came,
Oh, that fateful day,
The lumberjacks came.

They slashed, they thrived,
They did,
I saw,
Tree stumps galore.

By the end of this massacre,
Not many of us left,
I know, I know,
Not many of us left, I know.

Frank Turner (14)
Ormiston Horizon Academy, Tunstall

Snowflake

S praying gentle ice
N ewly formed snow
O verlaying the sheets of white
W ondering where I'll land
F alling, gentle, slow
L anding finally upon the surface
A nd melting into triviality
K ept hidden below
E very flake of snow.

Tegan Cawley (14)
Ormiston Horizon Academy, Tunstall

A Gunshot

Traipsing through the dirt tracks,
Walking for three days,
My feet ache,
My legs ache,
My whole body aches,
German shouts ring out in my ears,
A gunshot,
A scream,
We stagger past her bloody body,
Mothers cover children's eyes,
I stop, she is beautiful.
A gunshot...

Eleanor Green (12)
Ormiston Horizon Academy, Tunstall

Do You Love Me Or Hate Me?

Some people love me,
Some people hate me,
It's a half and half choice,
Please don't betray me.

I'm only food,
You'll eat me anyway,
Don't be disgusted,
Please don't betray me.

Miah Brooks (14)
Ormiston Horizon Academy, Tunstall

Fire

I feel sad, I've lost most of my family to burning fire...
Houses and homes have been destroyed.
Screams and yelps, all around me.
Fur and bone, dead monkeys.
No food to eat.
Smoke, black smoke.

Natasha Smith
Ormiston Horizon Academy, Tunstall

An Olympian

Have you ever heard of me?
Simone Biles
I am flexible
I am strong
And I am a gymnast
I have won five medals
Four of them are gold
I just can't wait
To get more.

Sophie Poyser (11)
Ormiston Horizon Academy, Tunstall

Burning

A haiku

Bright red roaring flames
the Amazon rainforest,
yet no one helps us.

Precious Butler (14)

Ormiston Horizon Academy, Tunstall

Too Young

They say we are too young,
To know the horrors of the world we live in,
Too young to know what's happening around us,
Too young to know anyone else's pain,
And they are right.

We are too young,
To see the world torn to pieces,
By people who don't care,
And will never care,
About anyone but themselves.

We are too young,
To witness a boy attacked or beaten,
Just because of the colour of their skin.

We are too young,
To see someone teased or ridiculed,
For being gay,
Or transgender,
Or just for breaking the mould,
And daring to be different.

We are too young,
To know a friend driven to suicide.
Simply because no one noticed the signs
Or because no one could be bothered to help.

Too young,
To see children,
Just like us living in squalor and poverty,
Unable to afford an education,
And constantly hungry.

Too young to turn on the television and hear of another attack,
Of hundreds of more innocents killed,
Killed by a single person,
A single, mad person,
Who killed as easily as most people blink.
We are too young,
To see these things.
But they are happening.
And it's not us who should be stopping it.

It's you.
You who could make the difference.
You could save all the children,
Who die every year,
Simply because no one cared.

Ewan Harbord
Pakefield High School, Pakefield

Rufus

I can't believe my eyes
A tennis ball!

It is just so great
It is bouncy and well green
Slam,
Owen is home.

I go sliding over to him on the slippery, laminate floor
I can't run straight with excitement
and slippery surface combined
I may have tiddled on the floor a little
But I'm still young and not toilet trained so...

"Hewo! Hewo!"
I still can't figure out why he speaks to me as if I am a baby
I know I'm small
I know I'm ten weeks old
But I can understand fluent English

Ding! Ding! Ding!
That's all I can hear
I'm so very positive it is my dinner
So I try to jump onto the table to see
But my bones aren't fully developed yet
Bang! Flat on my face
Ouch!

Owen Carson (14)
Pakefield High School, Pakefield

A Bully's Victim

I'm praying every night,
From these haunts that show no light,
At school I have no luck,
I don't know why I was chose,
Everything inside me wants to close,
I was like in a bubble, nowhere to escape,
Nothing could help, nor Superman and his cape,
My locker was tipped out, my lunch money was took,
They took me down on how I look,
This stopped me from being taught,
I sat on my own,
Then it got noticed,
I knew then I didn't have to have the bad thoughts,
Before everything was a deafening silence,
Now I was free from the terrors,
I grew stronger, I told my parents, I told the school,
I found out it's better to tell someone sooner or later!

Ayva-Mai Claxton (11)
Pakefield High School, Pakefield

Seagulls

Have you ever thought about what it would be like to be a seagull?
To fly?
To look down on the world?
I heard you find us annoying, loud, dumb.

Well, think about our point of view,
The way you scream, shout, point and laugh.
You leave your litter, tricking us to pick it up.
You think you're funny, don't you?
You try to kill us you really do.
First, you drop food, I'm grateful to you.
Next, you drop plastic.
Wow, how rude!

Ryan Griffiths (14)
Pakefield High School, Pakefield

My Dog Mum

The key goes in the door,
my tail starts to wag.
In her hands,
there are loads of bags.
As she calls my name,
I feel shame.
I do a little wee
as she makes a cup of tea.
She sits down to say hello,
as I start to lick her toe.
I jump to give her a hug and kiss,
then I accidentally lick her lips.
Tori is the best owner,
without her, I'd be a loner.
I love her a ton,
she is my dog mum.

Tori Bellis (12)
Pakefield High School, Pakefield

Hot And Steamy

I couldn't believe my spout,
what was coming out
of poor old me.

It burns,
the liquid churns,
I get used every day.
Oh, the pain,
hurts me inside.

If I could have one wish.
I would stop the swish.
Why not be inventive and pour me into a dish?

The cup and saucer makes a clink,
the perfect drink, don't you think?

Darcey Crowe (11)
Pakefield High School, Pakefield

Soldier

S erving your country
O perating the battle
L iving life
D esert fighting
I fight for my country
E arly mornings
R isking my life.

Finley Oliver Gary Chase (12)
Pakefield High School, Pakefield

There's No Life

As I stood there looking around the room
I felt a horrible feeling.
The trees were blowing
my hands were shaking,
I was there looking for people.
"Anyone!" I shouted
but nothing.
Then, suddenly,
the floor started moving,
there was a loud bang.
The walls were collapsing all around
like cheese crumbling into a pan.
The windows were melting ice flooding the flat floor.
My space was invaded,
My life began to shrink.
The rays of light narrowed,
My remaining rays of hope dissolved.
Life, at one instant, disappeared into a single spot.

Hero Silverwood (11)

Rishworth School, Rishworth

Through Their Eyes

Why have they left me?
Where have they gone?
They promised to stay home
But now I am all alone.

My eyes are as big as the moon.
I am scared
Will they come home?
I am all alone.

Wait, what is that noise?
It sounds like thunder, it must be the boys.
They are back home,
I am no longer alone,

I wonder where they went
I wonder what they saw.
I hope they don't go away again
I don't want to be left alone.

They go, "Good girl"
And scratch my ears.
Give me treats,
I love my home.

William Whiteley
Rishworth School, Rishworth

129

Home

It started as a normal day at home,
Then things took a turn for the worst,
Our owners put us in a small box
And left us alone on the street.

We were cold, tired and hungry,
As the long day came to an end,
We cried and cried for days
But people just walked on through the rain.

On the third day,
A kind face peeped into our box,
She stroked us and gave us food,
Rescue had finally come.

She took us home and we explored,
It was warm and safe,
With plenty of toys,
Suddenly, we realised we had found our forever home.

Ruby Jones (12)
Rishworth School, Rishworth

I Went To Sea

I am a little plastic cup,
That sat upon a shelf,
One day I was taken off the shelf
And filled with lots of coffee.

They took me to the seaside
And left me in the bin,
Then a nasty, tempestuous wind came
And I was blown away to sea.

I broke up into little pieces
And spread across the bay,
A turtle came to see me one day
And nibbled my brown soggy edges.

It ate me up
And swam away,
So now I ask,
That you all try,

To take the time to see things,
Eye to eye.

Rhianna Lancaster (11)
Rishworth School, Rishworth

The New Baby

It was the day after my birthday,
I was sitting on the floor playing with my teddies.
Then I heard it, a deafening scream,
Little did I know a monster was about to enter my life.
I ran to the door to see Mummy, Daddy and a blanket.
"Hello, darling," I heard Mummy say, "meet your new sister!"
Sister? The words echoed in my head.
I didn't know what it was or why it was here.
But I knew it had to go back to where it came from.

Dorothy Davies (11)
Rishworth School, Rishworth

Listen!

Shush, shush, shush,
Hush, hush, hush
That's all they ever say
I try to tell them what I want
But they all just turn away
When I scream because I'm hungry
No one ever cares
When I howl because I'm tired
I'm left alone upstairs
How can I make them understand?
That at the age of one
I might just need a helping hand
Shush, shush, shush,
Hush, hush, hush
That's all they ever say.

Olivia Hambling (11)
Rishworth School, Rishworth

Swords Ready

Our swords are at the ready
The strong soldiers are ready
They have their shin pads on
Their helmets are on
Their armour is on
We are going against our rivals
Going to war
The captain said, "Attack!"
Let the battle commence
We don't know what will happen
We were getting battered and bruised
In the end, we won and we claimed victory
Victory in hockey and home to celebrate.

Lily Elizabeth Edmunds (12)
Rishworth School, Rishworth

The Last Day Of The World

A million thoughts ran through my head
Will I be alive or just dead?
Twenty-four hours, what will I be?
Only a matter of time, I would see
A helpless boy with no destiny
Stop at nothing to defeat his enemy.

Harry Ashford (11)
Rishworth School, Rishworth

The Stroll Through Town

It was morning and the sun shone bright,
I felt younger, braver, brighter, alright.
As the wind swayed my braids back,
I heard the sound of the children playing in the park,
The sun became sad and the sky became dark.
I thought it would be a bright day,
Then the poor day barked rain, rain, like pounding fists on
my head, shoulders and back.
The rain had stopped pounding like fire,
It started to disappear floating higher and higher.
As I used my fingernails to comb through my hair,
Cars started to introduce the moaning sounds of their
engines here and there.
The trees started to quiver as they sway side to side,
It got hotter and hotter, the leaves had fried.
As it became darker the street light became yellow,
It became quiet, I could hear my voice echo.
When it was pitch-black the moon had entered,
People tucked in their kids and their eyes had sheltered.
In the middle of the night it sounded like ants across a
cloud,
As I happily walked forward I couldn't hear a single sound.

Keirabelle St Pierre
Sheldon School, Chippenham

Save Our Planet

S ometimes I think our world is beautiful
A nd sometimes I think it is cruel
V ending machines
E lectronic devices

O dd coloured socks
U nite us all
R emember one piece of

P lastic remains on our planet for years
L et's all come together
A nd change so it doesn't get worse
N ow take your time to recycle
E veryone has a chance
T o turn this crisis around.

Milla Smith

Sheldon School, Chippenham

Present

I am pulled out of a box,
These people say, "Merry Christmas!"
And I am given to this boy
To make him happy and bring him joy,
I love my new life.

I get taken for walks
And bought new toys,
I love my new owner,
I love my new life.

My owner is interested
But I am not,
When I see him, I wag my tail
But he doesn't care,
It doesn't bother me,
It's not his fault,
But, maybe tomorrow he'll play with me,
I love my new life.

My food bowl is empty
And they do not care,
My ribs are visible
And, yet, they don't care,
I love my new life.

As a massive surprise,
My owner can drive,

Oh, how much he's grown
And, so have I,
Maybe he will start to care.
I love my new life.

He drove me to a forest
And threw a stick for me to fetch,
By the time I got it, he wasn't there,
Maybe I'm just silly, maybe it's a game,
Maybe he is still there, looking for me,
Well, I believe that he will come back,
I'll just lay here until that,
I love my new life.

Well, I'm cold now, shivering in the rain,
When will he come and put me out of this pain?
I tried to be good,
But not good enough
And there I died, patiently waiting,
While my owner threw me away like a piece of trash,
I love my new life.

Harley Donovan (15)
The Sandon School, Sandon

No Comment

"Today is 5th April, 2019. 17:27pm. Can you account for your whereabouts that evening?"

Cold. The bench was damp.
"Stop hogging it! Pass it here."
Coughing. It's strong.
"These flavours are loud."

"Tell us what happened. We cannot catch him without your help."

Sullivan.
In the shadows. Lurking. Waiting. Waiting for us to split apart, to be vulnerable.
Why is he running?

"What is your involvement with the 'Everywhere Unknown' gang?"
"No comment."
"Are you involved?"

It's not a gang. It's family. My family.
I grew up with them. They were there when she left. They were there when he never was. They were there when I tried to jump.

"No comment."

Luca Evangelista (14)
The Sandon School, Sandon

The Bully

When I wake up in the morning,
My mind fills with negative thoughts,
The fear of school runs through my body
While I find I am here, alone in this daunting house,
The house remained a corpse and so did my body,
All I knew was that I was alone once again.

My steps into school were like my steps into death,
Going slower and slower,
I knew I had nothing left.

When someone was nice it made me snap,
It filled me with anger and gave me a malevolent smile,
The tears that filled her eyes made me sorry,
But all I knew was that I was alone once again,
Inside, I truly am sorry.

I had a lion inside me, eating me up,
Making me feel like I wasn't enough,
I knew I was a bully
But all I wanted was some love.

Georgina Sewell (14)
The Sandon School, Sandon

Beyond The Scene

You're good at everything,
Feels like I've never been you,
Smiling through the screen,
I've never been seen.

I want to be what they see,
Hiding behind masks they create,
Wanting to be the best I can be.

No one knows how I actually am,
Everyone loves the persona,
I can't take it but they will not accept the real me,
I've never been seen.

Stepping on the stage, astonished
By all the stars shining,
Each valuable, never withering,
They stand strong, supporting
And loving my mask,
I wander through the garden,
Lost in my own fantasy,
I will never be seen,
I've never been seen.

Amy Stone (15)
The Sandon School, Sandon

Sticky And Brown

Oh, why don't people like me?
Maybe it's because I'm sticky and brown,
I always get left
On the shelves in shops in town.

Oh, why don't people like me?
Maybe it's because I smell,
People always just ignore me,
Oh well.

Oh, why don't people like me?
Maybe it's the way I spread,
So sticky and thickly,
Smothered all over your bread.

Oh, why don't people like me?
Maybe it's the way I taste,
Contained in a jar,
A sticky, brown paste.

Oh, why don't people like me?
They always call me bad,
My real name is Marmite,
It leaves me feeling sad.

Liam Hodgson (14)
The Sandon School, Sandon

The Rescue

Is there enough time?
If only she listened,
She had enough warnings.

Do I have enough time?
It's time to put training to real life,
Finally, I reached the water from the sand,
Just a few more strokes.

Does she have enough time?
She looks lifeless, even lost her voice,
Reaching the sand brings voices I'm glad to hear,
She has to make it.

Quick, silent breaths break the fear,
If only she'd stayed on the beach,
If only she could swim,
I wouldn't have to rescue her,
But that is my job,
My question was answered,
There was enough time.

Faye Bentley (14)
The Sandon School, Sandon

Injustice

The days of judgement,
The strike of the hammer,
The blow of the horn,
My influence the sinister fin of a thorn,
Have they not laid witness to my might?
Or am I but a blight?

The day of reckoning,
Centuries of sightless eyes and ignorance,
Blood spilt but no grievance,
Am I a plague, an infection
Or a damnation?

The binding of justice,
The days of relief.

"Are you not the stealer of guiltless lives?
Have you not caused the suffering of those,
Who have died?"

And, I replied,
"Who am I
But a word in a poem?"

Oliver Guy Newton Agar (14)
The Sandon School, Sandon

Unexpected Witness

It's Monday yet again,
All the kids mope in,
The class, miserable,
Kicking occurs under the table.

They finally settle in,
The English lesson begins,
Not at the back of class,
The geek's just been flopped.

Fifth period rolls in,
The next class begins,
They all stare at me,
Their eyes thin.

The bell rings,
They all leave,
Just me and my hands ticking away,
Waiting for the loneliness to wither away.

By myself, I stare,
The classroom bare,
Twelve hours 'til the kids come in
And settle in their chairs.

Samuel Panks (14)
The Sandon School, Sandon

Marmite

I'm a very controversial food,
You may hate me or love me,
You can spread me
Or lick me off the knife,
I sit on the shelf a lot.

Alone.

I don't get a lot of attention,
I just stand and get looked at,
Sometimes, I'm loved,
Other times, I'm a disgust.

I need a makeover,
A new start,
Maybe then you'll love me
And take me home,
I'm quite nice compared to my friends,

Bovril and Vegemite,
They're also quite bossy,
Standing at the front.

I cause arguments,
Family ones to be precise.

Mollie Prior (14)
The Sandon School, Sandon

Addiction

Pick up the pill,
Plumes of smoke,
The world is spinning,
Woke,
Your vision, blurred,
Words, slurred.

Look into their eyes,
The warm feeling inside,
The way they speak has your tongue-tied,
Quick, they're looking, flash inside,
You need this person to stay alive.

I come in many shapes and forms,
A villain in disguise,
Try to get rid of me,
But, I'll be on your mind.

This obsessive feeling,
Do you accept your mission?
I am your bad habit,
I am addiction.

Rachel Ghachaniu (15)
The Sandon School, Sandon

The Trio

Why won't they -
As I walk down the street,
I look to my right,
There is sadness.
I blend in, we all blend in,
The three of us,
The trio.
People look at me, only in pity,
I will never know why,
Walking down the streets with your friends is normal...
Right?
I talk to them all the time,
The stares I get on a daily basis concern me,
They aren't always with me,
It is just sometimes me,
My violent self,
Why won't they get out of my head?

Sophia Pilgrim (14)
The Sandon School, Sandon

Autumn Falls

Springtime, blooming,
My leaves growing,
Body inhabited by a squirrel, climbing,
Everything around changing.

Summer arrives, sap dripping,
My trunk shrinking,
Blistering heat burning,
Everything coming to an end.

Autumn materialising,
My body drooping,
Lonelier than ever,
Darkness appears.

Winter droning,
Fearful mind,
Blistering white everywhere,
Nothing more to do other than die.

Kade Silverman (14)
The Sandon School, Sandon

Escape

He wants to escape,
Too much fighting,
Too much war,
Too much hate,
He wants to go and find a mate,
He wants to escape,
Always scared,
Always hurt,
He feels like everything is a blur,
Watching his team pass away,
He just wants to run away.

Owen Griffin (14)
The Sandon School, Sandon

Depressed Pineapple

Born from the ground,
Hated by all,
Losing our families,
This needs to end,
For, we are pineapple
And pizza is our friend.

Henry Walker (14)
The Sandon School, Sandon

The Dying Planet

A haiku

The pain sifting in,
I can't succumb the pressure,
When will it all stop?

Joshua Jones (14)

The Sandon School, Sandon

Through The Motions...

I think back,
Back to the past,
Back to the last time I felt
Something...
Anything.
This thing I sing,
Drags me deep,
Drags me down, below the depths
Of my consciousness, I...
I take my breath,
Thinking of my death.
Depressed.
Diagnosed age fourteen,
And I wasn't keen to be seen
And it wasn't a dream.
I just wanted to be me.
I was mean, cruel,
An absolute fool.
Letting people down all around,
Until loser, loner, alone forever I was crowned.

Drowning in tears until all hope was lost,
Hopeless, helpless, all at what cost,
Hope was lost because I was lost,
Broken because my heart was broken
And there was no hope to be mended,
dented or healed.